Check Your IQ

The UK Mensa Puzzle Editors

Ken Russell & Philip Carter

foulsham

LONDON • NEW YORK • TORONTO • SYDNEY

Acknowledgements

We are indebted to our wives, both named Barbara, for checking and typing the manuscript, and for their encouragement in our various projects.

foulsham
Yeovil Road, Slough, Berkshire, SL1 4JH

ISBN 0-572-01807-X

Phototypeset in Great Britain by Typesetting Solutions, Slough, Berks.
Printed in Great Britain by Cox & Wyman Ltd., Reading, Berks.

Contents

Introduction

About the Authors

Ken Russell is a London surveyor and is Puzzle Editor of the *British Mensa Magazine*, a magazine which is sent to its 40 000 British members monthly.

Philip Carter is a JP and an Estimator from Yorkshire. He is Puzzle Editor of *Enigmasig*, the monthly newsletter of the Mensa Puzzle Special Interest group.

About Mensa

Mensa is a Social Club for which membership is accepted from all persons with an IQ (Intelligence Quotient) of 148 or above. This represents the top 2% of the population. Therefore one person in 50 is capable of passing the entrance test, which consists of a series of intelligence tests.

Mensa is the Latin word for 'table'. We are a round-table society where all persons are of equal standing. There are three aims: social contact amongst intelligent people; research in psychology; and the identification and fostering of intelligence.

Mensa is an International Society and has 102 000 members of all occupations: clerks, doctors, lawyers, policemen, industrial workers, teachers, nurses, etc.

Enquiries to: **MENSA FREEPOST**
Wolverhampton WV2 1BR,
England.

MENSA INTERNATIONAL
15 The Ivories,
6-8 Northampton Street,
London N1 2HV,
England.

What is IQ

IQ is the abbreviation for Intelligence Quotient. The dictionary definition of quotient is 'the number of times one quantity is contained in another'. The definition of intelligence is 'intellectual skill', 'mental brightness', 'quick of mind'.

When measuring the IQ of a child, the child would attempt an intelligence test which had been given to thousands of children, and the results correlated so that the average score had been assessed for each age group. Thus, a child who at eight years of age obtained a result expected of a ten-year-old, would score an IQ of 125 by the following simple calculation:

$$\frac{\text{Mental age}}{\text{Chronological age}} \times 100 = \text{IQ}$$

$$\therefore \frac{10}{8} \times 100 = 125 \text{ IQ}$$

This does not apply to adults, whose assessment would be based on results correlated to known percentages of the population.

A child with a high IQ would have a great advantage at school with his or her studies, as understanding of lessons would be easily absorbed, but, in itself, a high IQ is not a key to success in later life. More important would be the qualities of competitiveness, personality, ambition, determination and temperament. In most walks of life, however, problem-solving is encountered and a person with a high IQ is well adapted to be successful in this field.

The average IQ is, obviously, 100. The population can be split roughly into three groups: 50% would be between 90 and 110, 25% would be above 110 and 25% would be below 90.

Until recently, Intelligence Tests have been mainly related to knowledge of words, but with the advent of the increasing larger proportion of immigrants to Britain, whose knowledge of English would not be expected to be of a high standard, there is a swing towards Culture free tests. These are tests that use logic rather than word knowledge, so that diagrams are used instead of words. This makes no difference to the outcome, as spacial understanding and logical reasoning are good guides to one's degree of intelligence. These tests also have been standardised.

The eight tests which have been specially compiled for this book have not been standardised, so an IQ assessment has not been given. They are intended for practice for readers intending to take IQ tests in the future, and a guide is given as a check of success in undertaking each of these eight separate tests. There is also a further accumulated score for performance in all eight tests.

It is now considered that one's IQ factor has a hereditary basis, but that it is possible to improve slightly by practice with IQ tests, but only marginally. Generally speaking, the IQ factor remains constant throughout one's life, trailing off slightly with age.

How to use this book

The book consists of eight separate tests, each of 50 questions. The tests are of approximately the same degree of difficulty. It is suggested that you tackle each test separately and note your score, after checking your answers against those given at the end of each test. A scoring chart for each test is also shown, one mark being awarded for each correct answer.

Each further test taken should show a slight improvement in your score, as practice will improve performance.

The total can then be taken for the eight tests and checked against the total scoring chart, shown below and also at the end of the book.

Each test has a time limit of 120 minutes which must not be exceeded.

Notes The answers to some of the questions have been explained. You may find these explanations useful if you are 'stuck' on certain types of question.

In questions where you are required to find a missing word, the number of dots shown is equal to the number of letters in the word that you are looking for.

Total scoring chart for the eight tests

160–199	Average
200–239	Good
240–319	Very Good
320–359	Excellent
360–400	Exceptional

Test 1

1 Which of the tiles A to H will fit logically into the
   space?

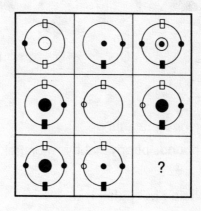

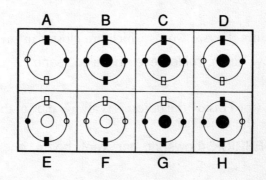

2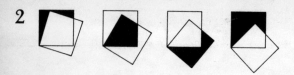

Which option below continues the sequence above?

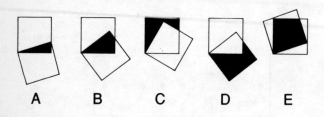

3 Which is the odd one out?

bitch, hound, puppy, tabby, mongrel

4 Epistle is to letter as epithet is to:

quip, name, speech, incident, archetype

5 Underline the two words which are closest in meaning.

low, flush, ruffle, level, develop, sane

6 Which word inside the brackets is always part of the word outside the brackets?

DERRICK (bowsprit, oar, vent, boom, anchor)

7 Place two three-letter 'bits' together to equal hog cured as bacon.

sco, fli, tia, por, tor, tch

8 Underline the name given to a group of owls.

murmuration, parliament, rafter, pace, wisp

9 If femur is to leg, then carpus is to which of these?

wrist, shoulder, arm, foot, pelvis

10 Underline which of these five words goes together with clip, weight and cup.

dance, strand, charm, chase, break

11 Here are five sets of faces.

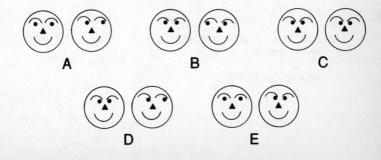

Which pair below completes the set?

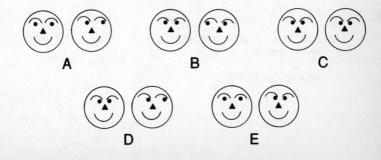

A   B   C

D   E

12 How many minutes before 12 noon is it, if one hour ago it was three times as many minutes after 8 a.m.?

13 Which of A, B, C, D or E is the odd one out?

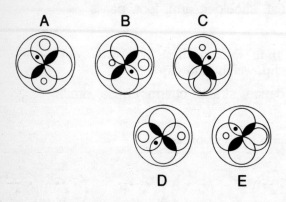

14 Which of these is the odd one out?

15 Insert a word that completes the first word and starts the second word.

win . . . . time

16 A B C D E F G H

Which letter is two to the left of the letter immediately to the right of the letter two to the right of the letter immediately to the right of the letter which is four letters to the left of the letter immediately to the right of the letter E?

17 Insert the missing number below.

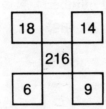

18 Underline the two words which are opposite in meaning:

despondent, autocratic, optimistic, nostalgic, cautious, steadfast

19 Underline the two words which mean the same:

travel, distrain, revolve, seize, vanish

20 Which word inside the brackets is never part of the word outside the brackets?

MAIGRE (vegetables, fish, tripe, eggs)

21 Which word means the opposite of bounteous?

hypothetical, niggardly, liberal, rewarding, grateful

22 Underline the odd name:

Hoover, Kennedy, Bolivar, Jefferson, Eisenhower

23 Find the missing number:

79, 87, ? , 89, 83,

24

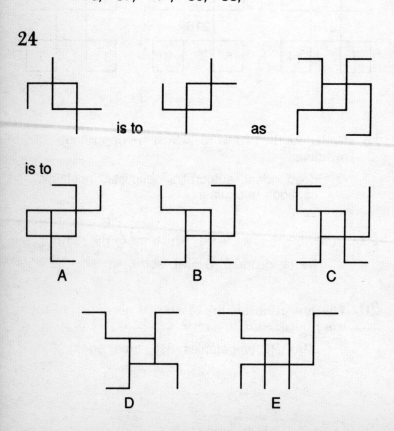

is to _____ as _____

is to

A   B   C

D   E

25 Which word inside the brackets is closest in meaning to the word in capital letters?

DETACH (specify, separate, withhold, uncover, reserve)

26

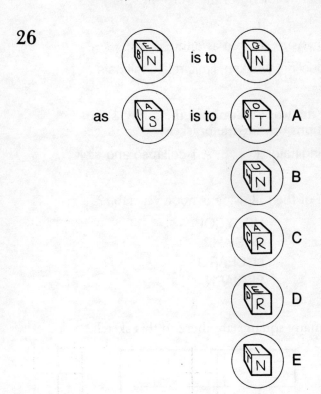

27 Which of these is the odd one out?

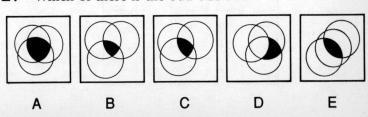

28 Here are six synonyms of the word 'fasten':

chain, connect, secure, attach, bolt, grip

Take one letter from each word, in order, to spell out a further synonym of the word 'fasten'.

29 Abridge is to shorten as dilute is to:

decline, weaken, limit, relax, mitigate

30 Insert the word that means the same as the definitions outside the brackets.

originator (. . . . . . .) collapse and sink

31 Which of the following is not a vegetable?

HRCYCOI
CNSIAHP
LCCEARO
SPRIAPN

32 How many squares are there in this sketch?

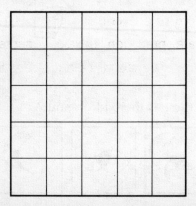

33 Underline the two words which are opposite to each other.

> treelike, hyperborean, southern, windward, eerie

34 Solve the anagram (one word):

> bare miles

35 Which word means the same as grampus?

> dolphin, grandpa, intruder, school, cat

36 Which word continues this sequence?

> square, pentagon, hexagon, septagon, ? ,

Choose from: nonagon, octagon, decagon, polygon

37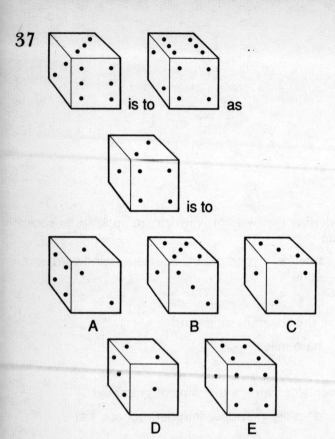

is to ... as ... is to ...

A   B   C

D   E

38 Which of A, B, C, D or E is the odd one out?

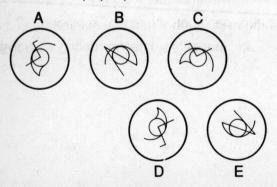

A   B   C

D   E

39

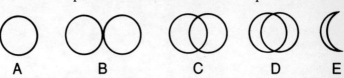

Which option below continues the sequence above?

A   B   C   D   E

40 Here are six antonyms of the word 'obliterate':

construct, form, make, establish, generate, formulate

Take one letter from each word, in order to spell out a further antonym of the word 'obliterate'.

41 Which is the odd one out?

subscription, money, bonus, rebate, stipend

42 Which two letters complete this sequence?

ND, ND, ESD, NES, RS, ID, ? .

43 What is the next number in this sequence?

1, 3, 8, 19, 42, 89, ? ,

44 Insert a word that completes the first word and starts the second word.

DRAW . . . . . . HEAD

45 Solve the anagram (one word):

failed us

46 What is a mutchkin? Is it:

(a) a measure   (b) a sprite
(c) mutton   (d) a baby   (e) a muscle?

47 Insert a word that means the same as the words outside the brackets.

tree (. . . . .) aircraft

48 Which of squares A to H is the missing one?

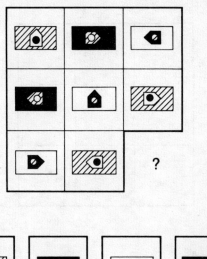

?

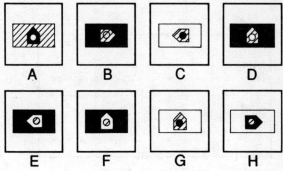

49 Which of the tiles A to H will fit logically into the space?

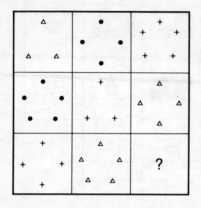

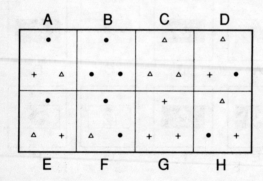

50 Which of the tiles A to H will fit logically into the space?

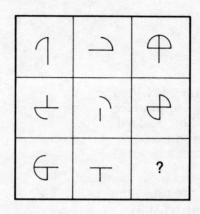

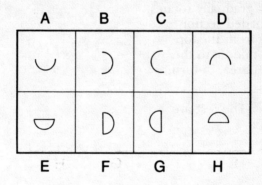

Answers Test 1

1 G. (Column 2 is added
to Column 1 to produce
Column 3. Row 2 added
to Row 1 produces
Row 3.)

2 B. (There are two
squares. One remains
stationary. The second
square gradually rotates.
The shaded section
moves from the top
to the middle to the
bottom area, in turn.)

3 tabby (The rest are
dogs.)

4 name

5 flush, level

6 boom

7 flitch

8 parliament

9 wrist

10 chase   (These four words can all have the prefix 'paper'.)

11 D.   (There are four eye positions: left, right, centre and squint. D completes every possible pairing of the four eye positions.)

12 45 minutes.

13 B.   (A is the same as D, rotated and C is the same as E, rotated.)

14 D.   (The rest are identical but rotated to different positions.)

15 some

16 D.

17 34.
$$(9+14)\times(19-\ 7)=276$$
$$(18+\ 9)\times(14-\ 6)=216$$
$$(10+\ 7)\times(16-14)=\ 34$$

18 despondent, optimistic

19 distrain, seize

20 tripe

21 niggardly

22 Bolivar

23 81. (The differences are $+8$, -6, $+8$, -6.)

24 B. (The figures are flipped over vertically.)

25 separate

26 C. (They spell the words BENIGN and LASCAR.)

27 D. (In the others, the section common to all three circles is shaded.)

28 anchor

29 weaken

30 founder

31 LCCEARO.
(Anagram of **CORACLE**. This is a boat. The vegetables are chicory, spinach, parsnip.)

32 55.

33 hyperborean, southern

34 miserable

35 dolphin

36 octagon

37 E.   (The die rolls over one turn.)

38 C.   (A is the same as D, rotated and B is the same as E, rotated.)

39 C.   (The circle which starts on the right is moving over the circle which starts on the left, half a diameter at a time.)

40 create

41 money

42 UR.   (They are the middle letters extracted from the days of the week.)

43 184.   (Each of the numbers is doubled and 1, 2, 3, 4, 5, 6 is added in turn, so $89 \times 2 + 6 = 184$.)

44 bridge

45 fusilade

46 (a)

47 plane

48 D. (Each horizontal and vertical line of squares contains a black, a white and a striped section. The arrows point left, right and up in each line of squares.)

49 B.

50 C. (Column 1 is added to Column 2 to produce Column 3, but where lines or curves in Columns 1 and 2 coincide, they are deleted in Column 3. Similarly for the Rows.)

Scoring Chart for Test 1

20–24	Average
25–29	Good
30–39	Very Good
40–44	Excellent
45–50	Exceptional

Test 2

1 Which of the tiles A to H will fit logically into the space?

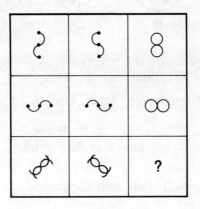

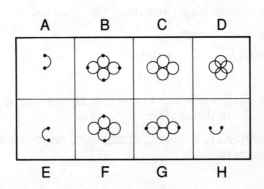

2

Which option below continues the sequence above?

   A   B   C   D   E

3 Which word inside the brackets is opposite in meaning to the word in capital letters?

    REAR (starboard, stern, bow, yard, poop)

4 Which word below goes together with age, rule and rod?

    rabbit, club, ball, eagle, albatross

5 What creature is missing from the brackets?

    hole (fox) trot
    feed (. . . . . . .) out

6 Which word inside the brackets is always part of the word outside the brackets?

    GARGOYLE (arms, spout, hat, spectacles, pince-nez)

7 Place two three-letter 'bits' together to equal a two-masted vessel.

    fal, iot, lug, gal, len, ien

8 If parapet is to roof, then fumarole is to which of these?

chimney, volcano, skylight, mountain, iceberg

9 Underline the name that is given to a group of hermits.

assembly, bench, caste, fraternity, observance

10 Which word below goes together with case, worm and mark?

coat, slide, pitch, station, jacket

11 Which of the shapes A to E is the odd one out?

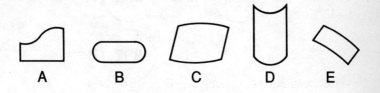

A   B   C   D   E

12 Fill in the missing number.

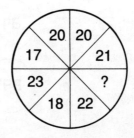

13 On glancing through your morning paper, you notice that four pages are missing. One of the missing pages is page 10. The back page of the newspaper is page 32. What are the numbers of the other three missing pages?

14 Underline the two words which are closest in meaning.

total, equate, compose, speak, compare, itemise

15

SKИ   is to   SЯN

as   ВPZ   is to   BPƧ   A

ВƧZ   B

BPZ   C

ƧPВ   D

ВƧƧ   E

16

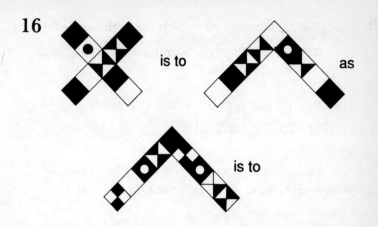

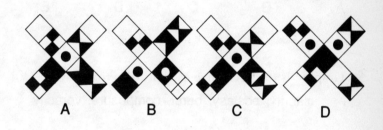

A B C D

17 Which word inside the brackets is never part of the word outside the brackets?

  MERINGUE (currants, egg, sugar, cream)

18 Which word, below, means the opposite of gaucherie?

  awkwardness, ugliness, suaveness, brilliance, insistence

19 Underline the odd word out.

  stalls, circle, scenario, fauteuil, box

20 Underline the two words which mean the same.

cursive, obstructive, flowing, repulsive, static

21 Find the missing number in the sequence:

31, 28, ? , 30, 31,

22 Which of A, B, C, D or E is the odd one out?

23 Graphic is to descriptive as rapture is to:

alacrity, ecstasy, burst, composure, voracity

24 Insert the word that means the same as the definitions outside the brackets.

noisy quarrel (. . . .) become ragged

25 Which is the odd one out?

calligraphy, artistry, chirography, writing, scribble

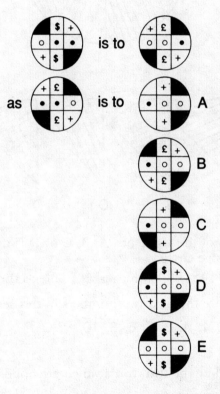

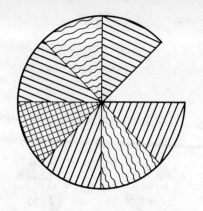

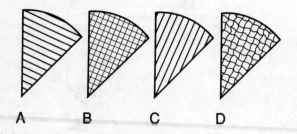

Which of the segments, A, B, C or D is missing from the above circle?

28 What are the next two numbers in this sequence?

2, 1, 4, 3, 6, 6, 8, 10, ? , ? ,

29 Underline the two words which are opposite to each other.

tapes, fauces, lips, taps, lupus

30 Which word means the same as scarab?

beetle, weapon, ruffian, ghost, dervish

31 Which word continues the sequence?

cesspool, damp-course, transome, eaves,

Choose from: reredos, moulding, loft, doorstep

32 Solve the anagram (one word):

rivet wine

33

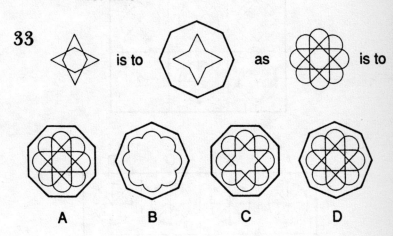

is to ... as ... is to

A   B   C   D

34 Fill in the missing word.

SEEN (LIKENESS) SILK

QUIT (. . . . .) YALE

35 Quixotic is to romantic as visionary is to:

idealistic, realistic, peace, reforming, belief

36 Insert the same number three times into this equation as it stands, to make it correct.

5 + 12 = 13

37 Which of the tiles A to H will fit logically into the space?

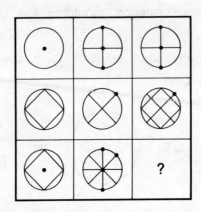

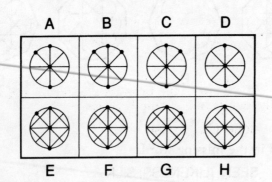

38 Which of A, B, C, D or E is the odd one out?

39 Here are eight synonyms of the word 'bogus':

false, phoney, dummy, forged, artificial, counterfeit, fraudulent, sham

Take one letter from each word, in order, to spell out a further synonym of the word 'bogus'.

40 Which is the odd one out?

joke, laugh, chortle, titter, snigger

41 Which word means the same as the two words outside the brackets?

conceal (. . . .) skin

42 Solve the anagram (one word):

some great

43 Place the word in the brackets that means the same as the words outside the brackets.

alone (. . . .) fish

44 What is a tiro? Is it:

(a) a jewel (b) a bird (c) a peasant
(d) a novice (e) a flume?

45 Insert a word that completes the first word and starts the second word.

chain . . . . bag

46

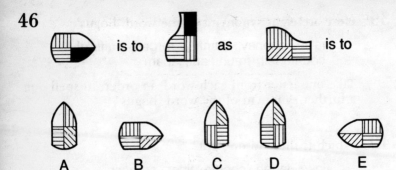

A **B** **C** **D** **E**

47 Which one of the following is not one of the seven virtues?

       THRYIAC
       CPEUNRED
       OGNTUYTL
       TAFIH
       DFERUITOT

48   DEED, NOON, OCEAN, SEED, ? ,

Which word below continues the sequence above?

    REAP, CAST, FLY, AUDIT, MINIM

49 Which of A, B, C, D or E is the odd one?

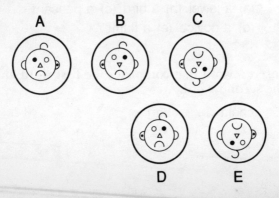

     A   B   C

          D   E

50 Which of the tiles A to H will fit logically into the missing space?

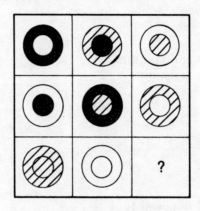

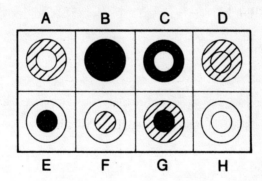

Answers Test 2

1   D.   (Rows and columns
      added and black dots
      deleted.)

2   B.

3   bow

4   eagle   (All four words
      can be prefixed by
      'golden'.)

5   chicken

6   spout

7   galiot

8   volcano

9   observance

10   jacket   (All four
      words can have the
      prefix 'book'.

11 A. (The only figure which has no symmetry, and also it has three straight lines, only one curved line, and a double curve.)

12 19. (Start at one '20' and, in a clockwise direction, jump alternate sectors adding one. Start at the other '20' and, in a clockwise direction, jump alternate sectors deducting one.

13 Pages 9, 23 and 24.

14 equate, compare

15 E.

16 C. (One strip is put across the other to form a cross so that the middle segment is common to both. All black areas change to white and all white areas change to black.)

17 currants

18 suaveness

19 scenario

20 cursive, flowing

21 31. (The number of days in each of the first five months of a non Leap Year.)

22 B. (A is the same as D, and C is the same as E, when black and white are reversed.)

23 ecstasy

24 fray

25 artistry

26 D.

27 B. (In opposite segments, the lines of the patterns are the other way round.)

28 10, 15. (There are two series: 2, 4, 6, 8, 10 and 1, 3, 6, 10, 15.)

29 fauces, lips

30 beetle

31 loft

32 interview

33 C. (The middle pattern is removed and encases the original figure without the middle pattern.)

34 EQUALITY (Anagrams.)

35 reforming

36 $5^2 + 12^2 = 13^2$

37 G.

38 D. (It does not contain a line. All other figures contain a line, a circle, a dot, a triangle and an arc.)

39 spurious

40 joke

41 hide

42 gasometer

43 sole

44 (d)

45 mail

46 A. (The original figure is turned on its end and changes to the second shape.)

47 GLUTTONY

48 AUDIT. (The first two letters of each word are the same as for the months December, November, October, September.)

49 B. (A and C are the same, with C upside down, D and E are the same, with E upside down.)

50 B.

Scoring Chart for Test 2

20–24	Average
25–29	Good
30–39	Very Good
40–44	Excellent
45–50	Exceptional

Test 3

1 Which of the tiles A to H will fit logically into the space?

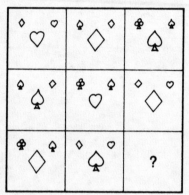

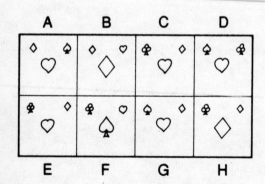

2 Which of A, B, C, D or E is the odd one out?

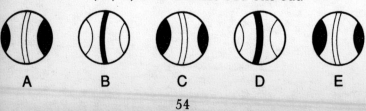

3 Insert the three missing words.

MANE		NAME
RATE	TARE	
	PALE	PLEA

4 Which word inside the brackets is opposite in meaning to the word in capital letters?

JAUNTY (wary, quiet, rough, staid, hostile)

5 Underline the name given to a group of princes.

pride, tiding, state, assembly, budget

6 Place two three-letter 'bits' together to equal the arm-pit.

lla, bes, axi, pue, oms, bro

7 If canal boat is to gondola, then privateer is to which of these?

coracle, junk, corsair, schooner, corvette

8 Underline which of these five words goes together with jack, board and guard.

magic, judge, switch, den, party

9 Which word inside the brackets is always part of the word outside the brackets?

LORGNETTE (legs, wheels, rudder, motor, handle)

10 Which or squares A to H is the missing one?

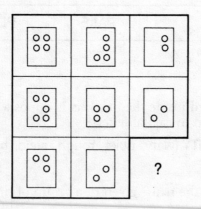

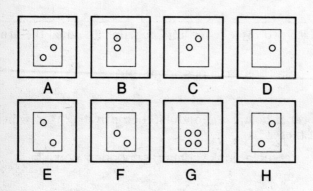

11   Which of A, B, C, D or E is the odd one out?

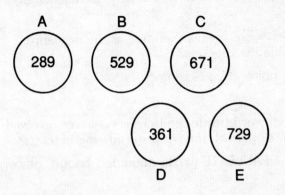

A   B   C

289   529   671

361   729

D   E

12   Which of A to E is the odd one out?

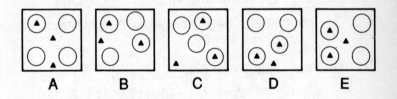

A   B   C   D   E

13   How many minutes past 11 a.m. is it, if two hours
ago it was three times as many minutes past 8 a.m.?

14   Underline the two words which are closest in
meaning.

infernal, malicious, rude, demonic, parasitic,
deranged

15 Which is the odd one out?

Dwight, Woodrow, Zachary, Cleveland, Ulysses

16 Which word means the same as the two words outside the brackets?

noise (. . . . .) intact

17 Which word inside the brackets is never involved with, or part of, the word outside the brackets?

EPAULETTE (wrist, shoulder, badge, officer)

18 Underline the odd word:

centime, moidore, brocket, piastre, pistole

19 Underline the two words which mean the same.

pendulous, finery, finesse, artifice, artifact

20 Find the missing number:

2, 12, 1112, ? , 132112, 1113122112,

21 Which word means the opposite of austral?

occidental, southern, northern, mountainous, hilly

22

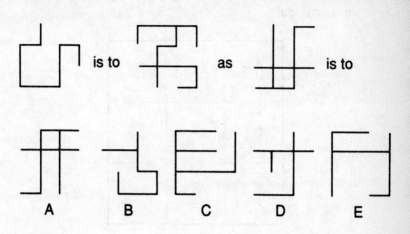

is to ... as ... is to

A   B   C   D   E

23 Read clockwise to find a word in each circle. You have to provide the missing letters. The two words are synonyms.

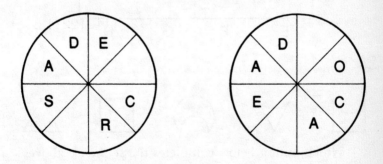

24 Which of the tiles A to H will fit logically into the missing space?

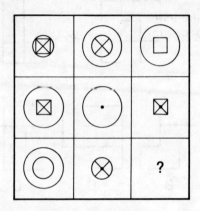

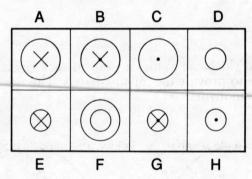

25

Which option below completes the sequence above?

A   B   C   D   E

26 Here are five antonyms of the word 'domesticated':

ferocious, savage, unbroken, untamed, wild

Take one letter from each word, in order, to spell out a further antonym of the word 'domesticated'.

27 Hilt is to sword as helve is to:

handle, whip, axe, knife, cup

28 Insert the word that means the same as the definitions outside the brackets.

crude dwelling (. . . . . .) kind of song

29 Which word means the same as jocose?

sad, plump, merry, plausible, capable

30 Underline the two words which are opposite to each other.

sallow, shallow, fallow, cultivated, hollow

31 What is the name given to a group of foxes? Is it:

**(a) a smuck (b) a stand (c) a sloth
(d) a skulk (e) a spring?**

32 Which word continues this sequence?

Duke, Marquess, Earl, Viscount,

Choose from: **Count, Prince, Squire, Baron, Lord**

33 Solve the anagram (one word):

liver base

34

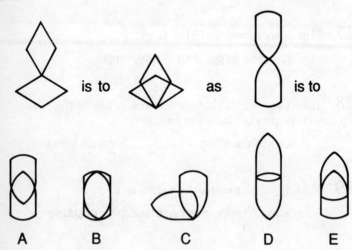

35   A B C D E F G H

Which letter is two to the right of the letter
immediately to the left of the letter three to the right
of the letter immediately to the left of the letter E?

36 Fill in the missing word.

ARCH (ENCROACH) CONE
GRIN (. . . . .) FINE

37

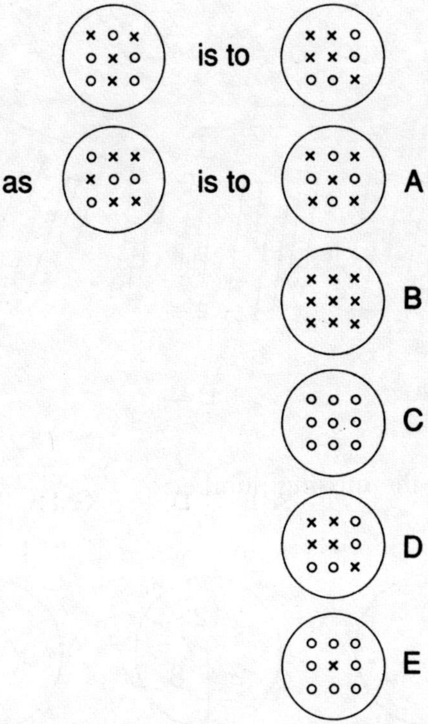

×o× is to ××o
o×o   ××o
o×o   oo×

as

o×× is to ×o× A
×oo   o×o
o××   ×o×

××× B
×××
×××

ooo C
ooo
ooo

××o D
××o
oo×

ooo E
o×o
ooo

38 Which of the options A, B or C, when fitted to the piece shown here, will form a perfect square?

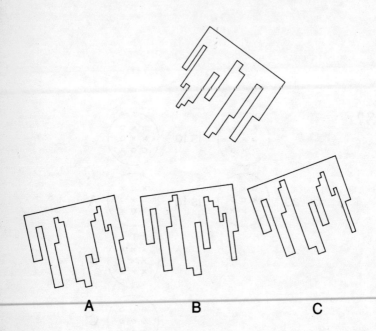

A   B   C

39 Fill in the missing number:

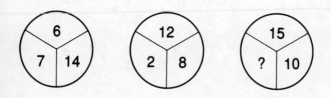

40 Place a word in the brackets that means the same as the words outside the brackets.

cloud (. . . . . .) halo

41 What is Shinto? Is it:

(a) a card game (b) a guard
(c) a religion (d) a dress (e) a scarf?

42 Solve the anagram (one word):

brief rake

43 Insert a word that completes the first word and starts the second word.

news . . . . . chase

44 Which of A, B, C, D or E is the odd one out?

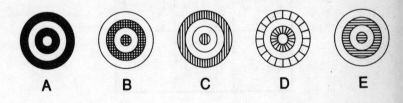

A   **B**   **C**   **D**   **E**

45 Which word inside the brackets is opposite in meaning to the word in capital letters?

PRUDENT (sagacious, open, permissive, extensive, improvident)

46 Which is the odd one out?

plait, tie, interlace, braid, intertwine

47 Dilemma is to quandary as plight is to:

danger, predicament, puzzle, confound, bewilderment

48 Which is the odd one out?

TFHORUERE
OTNWEO
SNEIVNEEN
FSIIVXE

49 Which of the tiles A to H will fit logically into the space?

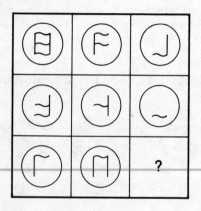

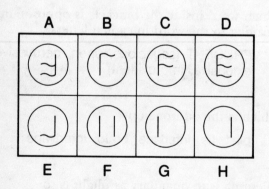

A   B   C   D

E   F   G   H

50 Which of A, B, C, D or E is the odd one out?

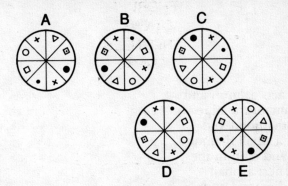

Answers Test 3

1 G.   (Each column and
row contains: a large
heart, diamond and
spade; a small diamond,
spade and club in the
left corner; a small
heart, diamond and
spade in the right
corner.)

2 E.   (A is a mirror image
of C and B is a mirror
image of D.)

3 MEAN, TEAR, LEAP
(The three words in
each line are anagrams
in alphabetical order.)

4 staid

5 state

6 axilla

7 corsair

8 magic   (These four words can all have the prefix 'black'.)

9 handle

10 D.   (Looking across and down, only circles common to both the first and second squares are carried forward to the third square.)

11 C.   (The rest are square numbers:

$17^2 = 17 \times 17 = 289$
$19^2 = 19 \times 19 = 361$
$23^2 = 23 \times 23 = 529$
$27^2 = 27 \times 27 = 729$)

12 A.   (In all the others there are two triangles in circles.)

13 30 minutes.

14 infernal, demonic

15 Cleveland. (It is the surname of an American President and the others are first names.)

16 sound

17 wrist

18 brocket

19 finesse, artifice

20 3112. (Each number describes, when spoken, the previous number.)

21 northern

22 E. (One put on top of the other forms a complete square grid.)

23 CRUSADER, ADVOCATE

24 B. (Add Column 1 to Column 2, similar symbols disappear, place answer in Column 3. Similarly for the Rows.)

25 E. (Each figure turns over and the curved line straightens. The resulting figure then moves three places to the right in the sequence.)

26 feral

27 axe

28 shanty

29 merry

30 fallow, cultivated

31 (d)

32 Baron

33 revisable

34 B. (The top figure falls to the bottom of the bottom figure.)

35 H.

36 INFRINGE (Anagrams.)

37 C. (Follow the same pattern in changing Xs and Os.)

38 C.

39 2. $(15 \times 2 \div 3 = 10)$

40 nimbus

41 (c)

42 firebreak

43 paper

44 C. (Because in the others, alternate segments are shaded.)

45 improvident

46 tie

47 predicament

48 SNEIVNEEN. (In the others, the first, third, fifth etc letters, and then the second, fourth, sixth etc spell out numbers that are consecutive.)

49 H. (Column 1 and Column 2 add to produce Column 3, but where lines or curves in Column 1 and 2 coincide, they are deleted in Column 3. Similarly for the Rows.)

50 B. (A is the same as D, rotated; C is the same as E, rotated.)

Scoring Chart for Test 3

20–24	Average
25–29	Good
30–39	Very Good
40–44	Excellent
45–50	Exceptional

Test 4

1 Which of the tiles A to H will fit logically into the space?

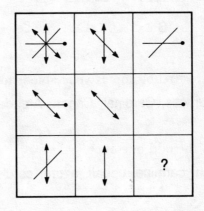

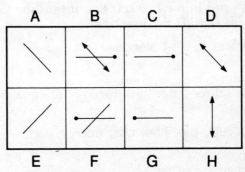

2

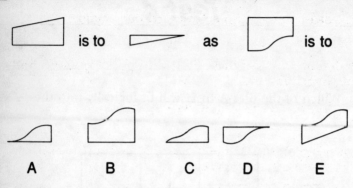

A   B   C   D   E

3 Grace is to Archbishop as Venerable is to:

Countess, Cardinal, Canon, Archdeacon, Bishop

4 Which is the odd one out?

cyan, carmine, cobalt, azure, cerulean

5 Place a word in the brackets that means the same as the words outside the brackets.

recline (. . . .) slender

6 Place two three-letter 'bits' together to equal Russian whips.

uls, uts, pro, kno, cks, tro

7 Underline the name that is given to a group of squirrels.

dray, erst, rush, convocation, dopping

8 If flatfish is to plaice, then bivalve is to which of these?

sea-horse, octopus, trout, oyster, squid

9 Underline which of these five words goes together with cup, finger and brick.

sand, dog, paper, wind, nugget

10 Which word inside the brackets is always part of the word outside the brackets?

TOURNEDOS (beef, cream, lamb, cheese, pork)

11

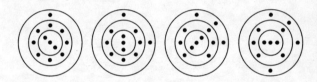

Which option continues the above sequence?

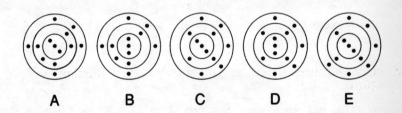

A   B   C   D   E

12 Which word inside the brackets is opposite in meaning to the word in capital letters?

PALE (attractive, happy, fair, bilious, florid)

13 Underline the two words which are closest in meaning.

valuable, sterling, distinct, shiny, new, genuine

14 Here are seven synonyms of the word 'decrease':

diminish, reduce, abate, shrink, curtail, dwindle, lessen

Take one letter from each word, in order, to spell out a further synonym of the word 'decrease'.

15

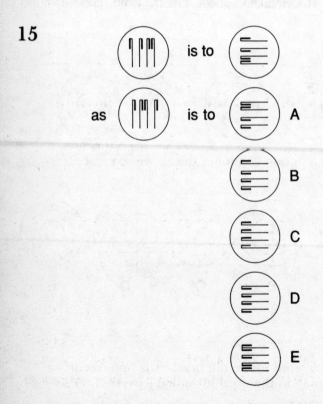

16 Which of the five boxes A, B, C, D or E, is most like the box on the left?

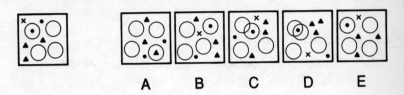

17 What is the missing number?

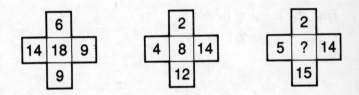

18 Read clockwise to find a word in each circle. You have to provide the missing letters. The two words are synonyms.

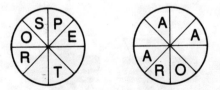

19 Which word inside the brackets is never part of the word outside the brackets?

QUADRILLE (cards, dance, four, playground)

20 Which word means the opposite of opulence?

sourness, poverty, riches, shiny, dull

21 Underline the odd word:

trapezium, octagon, ellipse, circle, cylinder

22 Underline the two words which mean the same:

hidden, canine, biscuit, doggo, cylinder

23 Find the missing number:

37, 41, ? , 47, 51,

24

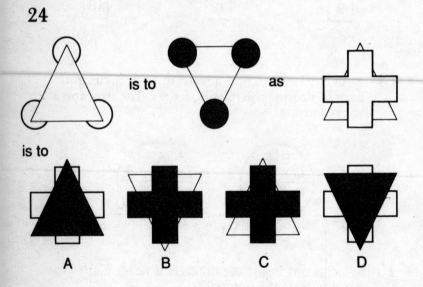

is to   as

is to

A   B   C   D

25 Which word inside the brackets is closest in meaning to the word in capital letters?

   PARAGON (fortress, section, pattern, leader, statement)

26 Insert a word that completes the first word and starts the second word.

   do ... less

27 Which of the tiles A to H will fit logically into the space?

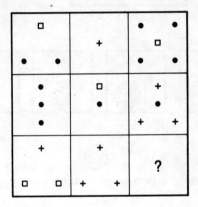

28 Which of squares A to D is the missing one?

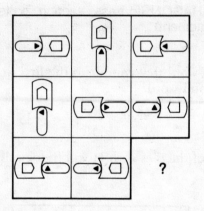

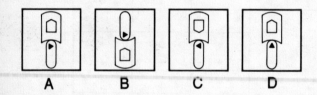

A   B   C   D

29 Underline the two words which are opposite in meaning.

trip, rive, strive, join, place

30 Which number should be placed at '?'.

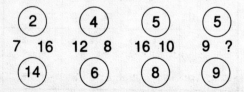

31 Solve the anagram (one word):

I sell a pub

32 Which word means the same as chough?

dry, rough, puff, crow, chewy

33 Which word continues this list?

Pat, Terry, Jackie, Hilary,

Choose from: Regina, Melanie, Bobby, Imogen

34 Which of the shapes A to E is the odd one out?

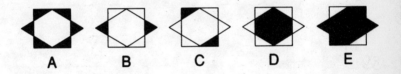

A   B   C   D   E

35 Fill in the missing number.

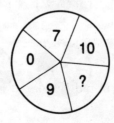

36 Which is the odd one out?

encyclopedia, novel, dictionary, lexicon,
thesaurus

37 Sierra is to mountains as savannah is to:

desert, valley, swamp, grassland, forest

38 Which of A, B, C, D or E is the odd one out?

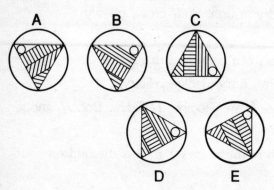

39

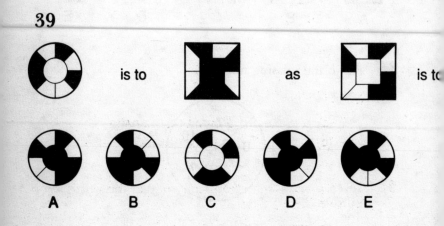

40 Insert the word that means the same as the definitions outside the brackets.

contrive (. . . . .) engrave or draw lines

41 Which of the following is not a bird?

NGOPIE
GEAMIP
LOOIRE
NTAUEP
OFCNLA

42 Solve the anagram (one word):

tribal ace

43 Insert a word that completes the first word and starts the second word.

false . . . . wink

44 What is a kraal? Is it:

(a) a game (b) a canal (c) a snake
(d) a village (e) a woodpecker?

45 Insert a word that means the same as the words outside the brackets.

grating (. . . . .) cook

46

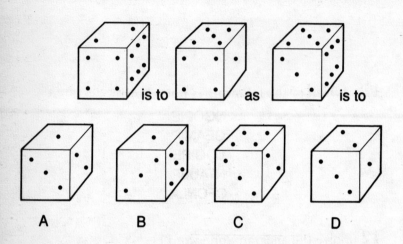

A   B   C   D

47 Fill in the missing number.

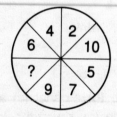

48 Underline the two words which are opposite in meaning.

worried, livid, confused, lifeless, delighted, irritable

49 Which of the tiles A to H will fit logically into the space?

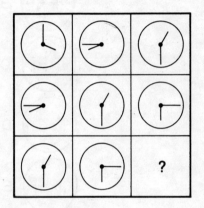

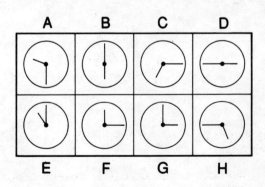

50

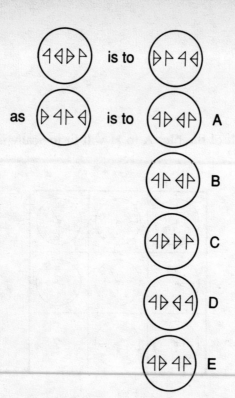

is to

as

is to

A

B

C

D

E

Answers Test 4

1 E.

2 A. (The figures added together form a rectangle.)

3 Archdeacon

4 carmine

5 lean

6 knouts

7 dray

8 oyster

9 nugget (These four words can all have the prefix 'gold'.)

10 beef

11 C.

12 florid

13 sterling, genuine

14 subside

15 A. (All hooks reversed.)

16 B. (It contains four circles (none of which intersect), three triangles, two dots (including one in a circle) and one cross.)

17 10. $(2 \times 15 \div 3 = 10$
and $5 \times 14 \div 7 = 10)$

18 PROSPECT,
PANORAMA

19 playground

20 poverty

21 cylinder

22 doggo, hidden

23 43. (Consecutive
prime numbers.)

24 D. The drawing is
turned over. The
figure at the back
comes to the front and
is dark instead of
white.

25 pattern

26 use

27 C. (Making each dot
= 1, each cross = 2
and each small square
= 3, Column 1 is
added to Column 2 to
equal Column 3.
Similarly for Rows.)

28 A. (So that each
horizontal and vertical
line of squares has
each component
pointing right, left and
upwards.)

29 rive, join

30 20. (When numbers outside the circles are multiplied together and divided by the numbers inside the circles, the answer is 4. i.e. $(9 \times 20) \div (5 \times 9) = 4$.)

31 plausible

32 crow

33 Bobby. (Unisex names.)

34 B. (A and D, C and E have reversed black and white.)

35 4. (Start at 10 and, moving round clockwise, jump alternate sectors, deducting one, then two, then three, then four.)

36 novel

37 grassland

38 C. (A is the same as E, rotated and B is the same as D, rotated.)

39 D. (Squares become circles, circles become squares, and black and white are reversed.)

40 hatch

41 NTAUEP. (Anagram of PEANUT. The birds are pigeon, magpie, oriole, falcon.)

42 calibrate

43 hood

44 village

45 grill

46 D. (The die is turned over twice.)

47 1. (Opposite sectors total 11.)

48 livid, delighted

49 E. (Each clock advances 4¾ hours left to right and top to bottom.)

50 A. (Each shape in the circle rotates, vertically, through 180°. If there is a lower diagonal line, this is removed; if there is no lower diagonal line, one is added.)

Scoring Chart for Test 4

20–24	Average
25–29	Good
30–39	Very Good
40–44	Excellent
45 50	Exceptional

1   Which of the tiles A to H will fit logically into the
    space?

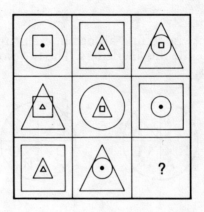

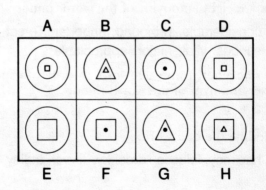

2 To which of the five boxes A, B, C, D or E, can a dot be added so that both dots meet the same conditions as in the box on the left?

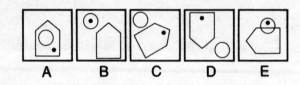

A　**B**　**C**　**D**　**E**

3 Read clockwise to find a word in each circle. You have to provide the missing letters. The two words are synonyms.

4 Here are eight antonyms of the word 'minor':

　　considerable, profound, important, great,
　　serious, vital, major, appreciable

Take one letter from each word, in order, to spell out a further antonym of the word 'minor'.

5 Underline the odd word:

　　hackney, felucca, droshky, flivver, trolley

6 Find the missing number:

　　169,　225,　?　,　361,　441,

7 Which word means the opposite of dulcet?

sweet, discordant, beautiful, shiny, musical

8 Underline the name given to a group of knaves.

deceit, pitying, rayful, desert, exhibition

9 Which of these is the odd one out?

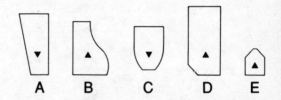

A   B   C   D   E

10 Fill in the missing number:

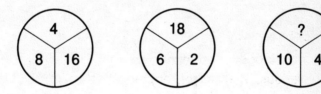

11 Flourish is to thrive as contrive is to:

succeed, scheme, prevail, accede, replace

12 Which word can be inserted in both sets of brackets to form other words with the addition of the letters on either side of the brackets?

S (. . .) H
C (. . .) H

13

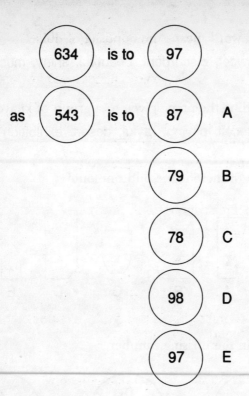

634 is to 97

as 543 is to 87 A

79 B

78 C

98 D

97 E

14

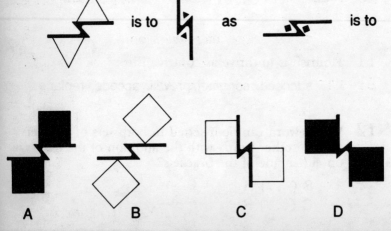

15 Underline the two words which are opposite in meaning.

urge, agree, enjoy, attack, secure, abhor

16 Insert the word that means the same as the definitions outside the brackets.

rod (. . .) unit of pressure

17 Solve the anagram (one word):

heed larks

18 Which word inside the brackets is always part of the word outside the brackets?

GUACAMOLE (avocado, pineapple, rum, brandy, peppers)

19 If flora is to floral, then fauna is to which of these?

vegetables, fish, animals, birds, seeds

20 Underline which of these five words goes with plane, sickness and side.

duster, sugar, rifle, man, top

21 Which letter continues this sequence?

T, L, H, Z, M, ? ,

Choose from: E, F, K, N, V

22 Which of squares A to H is the missing one?

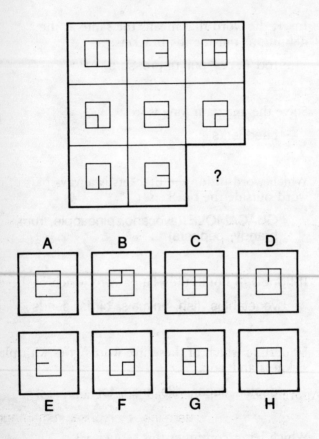

A   B   C   D

E   F   G   H

23 Which of A, B, C, D or E is the odd one out?

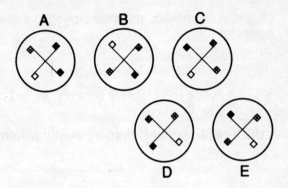

24 Which of A, B, C, D or E is the odd one out?

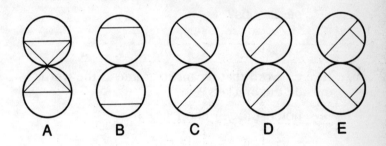

25 Apprehend is to understand as ascertain is to:

glean, learn, determine, memorise, remember

26 Which is the odd one out?

pentagon, pentathlon, pentode, penthouse, pentameter

27 Underline the two words which are closest in meaning.

    stagnate, complain, maunder, pester, thrash, meander

28 Which word inside the brackets is never part of the word outside the brackets?

    VULCANISE (rubber, harden, sulphur, iron)

29 What is a parashot? Is it:

    (a) a drug, (b) a parasite (c) a parakeet
    (d) a shot-putter (e) a marksman to shoot paratroops?

30 Insert a word that means the same as the words outside the brackets.

    horse (. . . .) chop

31 Which word means the same as welkin?

    drain, wrinkle, sky, storm, bells

32 Solve the anagram (one word):

    dead liver

33

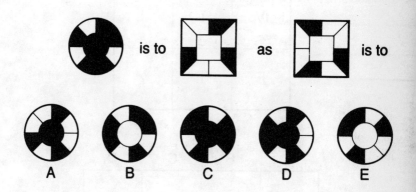

34 What is the decimal value of $\frac{5}{8} + \frac{7}{12} - \frac{5}{6}$?

35 Which word inside the brackets is closest in meaning to the word in capital letters?

PALATE (tongue, regal, taste, surface, board)

36 Which word means the same as the two words outside the brackets?

affirm (. . . . .) territory

37 Which of the tiles A to H will fit logically into the space?

MT	LI	N
IV	T	I
F	I	?

A	B	C	D
F	H	V	K
N	Z	M	I
E	F	G	H

38 Which box of the five boxes A, B, C, D or E, is least like the box on the left?

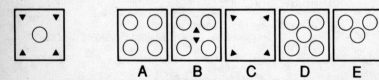

39 Fill in the missing number.

40 Which of the following is not a vehicle?

ROTESOC
IHTROCA
RAOTTCR
BNSMUIO
PCLEALS

41 Place two three-letter 'bits' to equal excessive fondness.

age, ade, ice, dot, pom, sol

42 Underline the two words which are opposite to each other.

doctor, mufti, Mohammedan, uniform, sword

43 Which word is part of this group?

mainsail, foresail, gaffsail, stormsail

Choose from: mistral, plimsoll, spinnaker, flotsam

44 Underline the two words which mean the same.

report, felon, artist, artisan, workman

45 Insert a word that completes the first word and starts the second word.

       partner .... **wright**

46 What are the next three circles in this sequence? Choose from A, B, C, D or E.

    A   B   C   D   E

47   A B C D E F G H

Which letter is two to the left of the letter immediately to the left of the letter which is four to the right of the letter immediately to the left of the letter which is two to the left of the letter D?

48 Vivace is to brisk as legato is to:

    short, fast, slow, smooth, loud

49 Which of A, B, C, D or E is the odd one out?

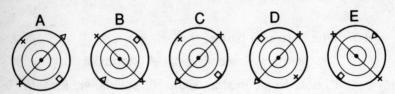

106

50 Which of the tiles A to H will fit logically into the space?

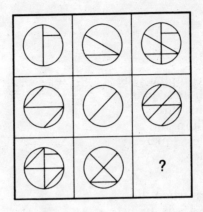

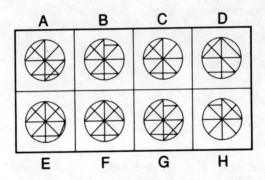

Answers Test 5

1   D. (This completes the set. The whole sequence now contains three large, medium and small, circles, squares and triangles.

2   A. (So that when the dot is added it is in both shapes and the circle contains one dot only.)

3   farcical, derisory

4   superior

5   felucca

6   289. (The sequence is 13^2, 15^2, 17^2, 19^2, 21^2.)

7   discordant

8   rayful

9 D. (In all the others, the arrow points to the narrowest side.)

10 25. (The square root of 25 × 4 = 10.)

11 scheme

12 LOT

13 E. (The first and second digits are added and the second and third digits are added.)

14 C. (The diagram turns upright, the small black squares change to large white squares.)

15 enjoy, abhor

16 bar

17 sheldrake

18 avocado

19 animals

20 man. (These four words can have the prefix sea)

21 E. (The first two letters of the sequence are each made up of two lines, the second two of three lines, the third two of four lines.)

22 F. (Looking across, any lines common in the first two squares disappear in the third square. Looking down, only lines common to the first two squares are carried forward to the third square.)

23 A. (B and E are the same but rotated; C and D are the same but rotated.)

24 D. (In all the others, the top circle is a mirror image of the bottom circle.)

25 determine

26 penthouse. (The prefix pent does not mean 'five'.)

27 maunder, meander

28 iron

29 (e)

30 hack

31 sky

32 daredevil

33 C.   (The first figure is
flipped over vertically.
Black changes to white
and white to black;
circles become squares
and squares become
circles.)

34 0.375

35 taste

36 state

37 C. (Each letter in the boxes is made up of straight lines. Each straight line scores 1 point. Column 2 is taken away from Column 1 to give Column 3, and similarly for the Rows. Thus,

$$6 - 3 = 3$$
$$3 - 2 = 1$$
$$3 - 1 = 2)$$

38 E. (It has an incomplete pattern. The others have both lateral and vertical symmetry.)

39 16. $(0 + 2 = 2,$
$2 + 2 = 4,$
$2 + 4 = 6,$
$4 + 6 = 10,$
$6 + 10 = 16.)$

40 PCLEALS. (Anagram of scalpel. The vehicles are scooter, chariot, tractor and omnibus.)

41 dotage

42 mufti, uniform

43 spinnaker

44 artisan, workman

45 ship

46 B.   (Splitting the circles into groups of three, the circles turn black one at a time from left to right and then white, one at a time, from right to left.)

47 B.

48 smooth

49 C.   (A is the same as D rotated and B is the same as E rotated.)

50 G.   (Rows and Columns added together.)

Scoring Chart for Test 5

20–24	Average
25–29	Good
30–39	Very Good
40–44	Excellent
45–50	Exceptional

Test 6

1 Select the missing tile from the six alternatives.

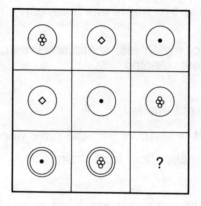

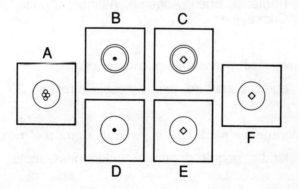

2 Which of these is the odd one out?

A   B   C   D   E

3 Underline the two words which are opposite in meaning:

prosaic, matchless, sentimental, mediocre, divergent, tangled

4   some, rail, made

Which word below goes with the three words above?

man, shake, fine, treat, train

5 Underline the two words which are closest in meaning:

Ruritania, Eden, Acheron, Atlantis, Utopia, Cockaigne

6 Which word means the opposite of egress?

egret, departure, exit, tigress, entrance

7 Underline the name that is given to a group of ravens.

kindle, gaggle, fraternity, unkindness, mute

8 Find the missing number:

21, 34, ? , 89, 144,

9 Underline the odd word:

lemming, racoon, limner, caribou, bubalis

10 Which of squares A to H is the missing one?

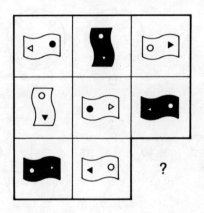

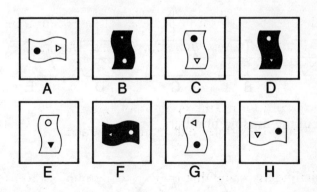

A   B   C   D

E   F   G   H

11 Which of these is the odd one out?

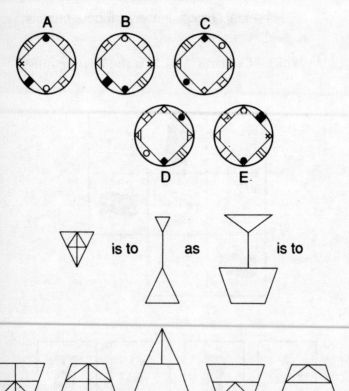

12

13 Fill in the missing number.

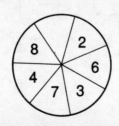

14 Here are six synonyms of the word 'gentle':

peaceful, bland, compassionate, merciful, benign, tender

Take one letter from each word, in order, to spell out a further synonym of the word 'gentle'.

15 What is the next number in this sequence?

23, 48, 84, 133,   ?   ,

16 Solve the anagram (one word):

cur as fuel

17 Underline which of these five words goes together with ache, ward and gammon.

door, pane, meat, target, struck

18 If scalene is to triangle, then trapezium is to which of these?

quadrilateral, circle, oval, hexagon, pentagon

19 Which word inside the brackets is always part of the word outside the brackets?

TRIGONOMETRY (solids, calculus, progressions, algebra, angles)

20 Which of these is the odd one out?

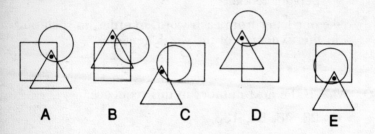

A **B** **C** **D** **E**

21 Which of the following is not a composer?

HMASRB
PHONIC
LMRHEA
ONERRI
GWREAN

22 Underline the two words which are closest in meaning.

lethargic, vituperative, sombre, virile, defamatory, corrupt

23 Which is the odd one out?

invalid, bedridden, void, inoperative, worthless

24

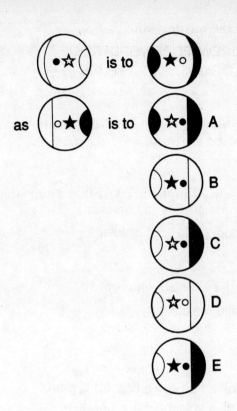

25

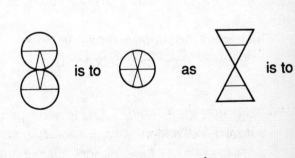

26 Fill in the missing word.

    DREW (FOREWORD) ROOF
    LOGO (. . . . .) PURE

27 Which word means a handle, a laughing stock, a bump and a barrel?

28 Place a word in the brackets that means the same as the words outside the brackets.

    dog (. . . . . .) soldier

29 Solve the anagram (one word):

    bite metal

30 What is a fulmar? Is it:

    (a) a fruit (b) a flag (c) a petrel
    (d) a volcano (e) a penguin

31 Which word means the same as mandrill?

    weapon, fish, tool, baboon, bird

32 Which word inside the brackets is never part of the word outside the brackets?

    SHILLELAGH (oak, cudgel, blackthorn, mulberry)

33 To which of the five boxes A, B, C, D or E, can a dot be added so that it meets the same conditions as in the box on the left?

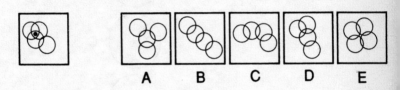

34 What is the missing number?

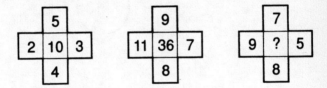

35 Below are eight antonyms of the word 'invincible'.

defenceless, weak, assailable, beatable, yielding, vulnerable, conquerable, powerless

Take one letter from each word, in order, to spell out a further antonym of the word 'invincible'.

36

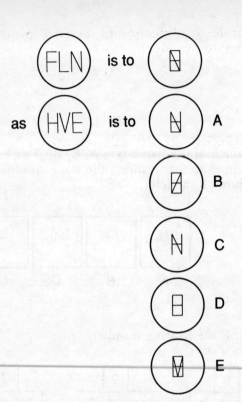

37

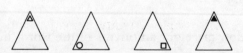

Which option below continues the sequence above?

38 Insert the word that means the same as the definitions outside the brackets.

distribute (. . . .) plank of wood

39 What number completes this sequence?

863937, 27216, 168, 48, 32,   ?

40 Tenterhooks is to suspense as enamoured is to:

labour, love, DIY, memory, confidence

41 Which word is part of this group?

squash, lacrosse, tennis, baseball

Choose from: yoga, canasta, pelota, pugilism

42 Insert a word that completes the first word and starts the second word.

fort . . . . . mare

43 Underline the two words which are opposite to each other.

soft, valuable, paltry, spongy, stringy

44 Underline the two words which mean the same.

harmless, perfect, replete, innocuous, sane

45 Place two-three letter 'bits' together to equal a lewd fellow.

gol, rib, man, ase, ald, and

46

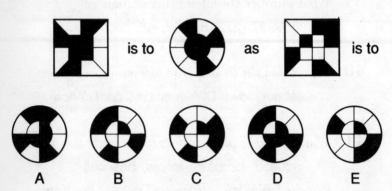

47   A B C D E F G H

Which letter is immediately to the right of the letter
three to the left of the letter immediately to the right
of the letter which is four to the right of the letter
which comes midway between the letters A and C?

48   Insert a word that completes the first word and starts
the second word.

        AS .... OR

49 Select the missing tile from the six alternatives.

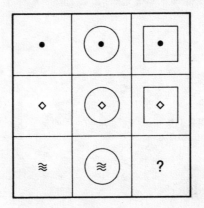

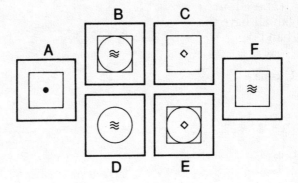

50 Which of these is the odd one out?

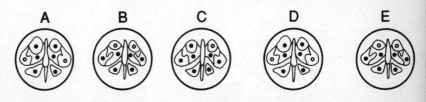

Answers Test 6

1 C.

2 B. (The others are rotations of the same figure.)

3 matchless, mediocre

4 shake. (These four words can all have the prefix 'hand'.)

5 Eden, Utopia

6 entrance

7 unkindness

8 55. (Fibonacci numbers – where each number is the sum of the two numbers preceding it.)

9 limner. (An illuminator of manuscripts.)

10 C.

11 B. (A and E are the same, but rotated and C and D are the same, but rotated.)

12 B. (The shapes at the ends of the vertical line are folded inwards.)

13 5. (Start at 2 and, moving round clockwise, jump alternate sectors, adding one each time.)

14 placid

15 197. (The differences are squares i.e. 5^2, 6^2, 7^2, 8^2.)

16 saucerful

17 door. (These four words can all have the prefix 'back'.)

18 quadrilateral

19 angles

20 B. (The only diagram in which the dot is not inside the circle; also the dot is in only one of the shapes.)

21 Renoir. (The composers are Brahms, Chopin, Mahler and Wagner.)

22 vituperative, defamatory

23 bedridden

24 C.

25 E. (The top part slides down over the bottom part.)

26 prologue (Anagrams.)

27 butt

28 terrier

29 timetable

30 (c)

31 baboon

32 mulberry

33 D. (So that the dot appears in three circles.)

34 28. $(9 + 5 \times 2 = 28$
and $7 \times 8 \div 2 = 28)$

35 fallible

36 E. (The letters in the
circles are placed on
top of one another.)

37 D.

38 deal

39 6. (All the digits
making up the
previous number are
multiplied together.)

40 love

41 pelota

42 night

43 paltry, valuable

44 harmless, innocuous

45 ribald

46 B. (The figure is
flipped over and
changes to circles.)

47 E.

48 SAIL

49 F.

50 C. (A and D are the
same; B and E are the
same.)

Scoring Chart for Test 6

20–24	Average
25–29	Good
30–39	Very Good
40–44	Excellent
45–50	Exceptional

Test 7

1 Which of the tiles A to H will fit logically into the space?

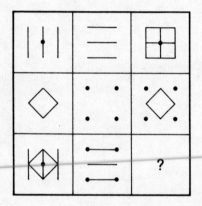

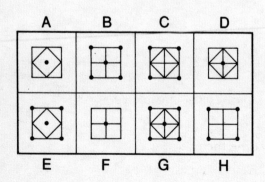

2

Which option below continues the sequence above?

A   **B**   **C**   **D**

3 What is the missing number?

4 Underline the two words which are opposite in meaning:

help, lead, subside, domineer, confute, intensify

5 Underline the name given to a group of hares.

plump, nide, muster, lepe, husk

6 Underline the odd word:

bustard, jackdaw, marabou, quetzal, lamprey

7 Find the missing number in this sequence.

10, 15, ? , 28, 36,

8 Which word means the opposite of recalcitrant?

calculating, chalky, furious, submissive, rebellious

9

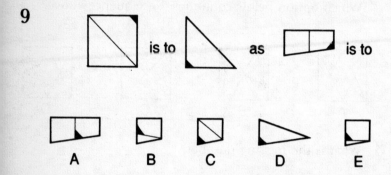

10 Which is the odd one out?

Mandingo, Masai, Maya, Zulu, Bantu

11 VACATE, PALATE, NEGATE, SIMILE, RELATE

Which word below would you choose to put with the words above?

ABROAD, NOVICE, STAMEN, LINEAR, SANITY

12 Insert the word that means the same as the two words outside the brackets?

pursuit (. . . .) breed

13 Which of the tiles A to H will fit logically into the space?

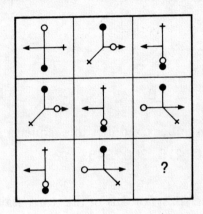

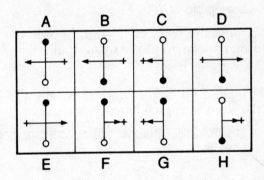

14

Which option below continues the sequence above?

A   **B**   **C**   **D**   **E**

15 Which number continues this sequence?

130, 215, 300, 345,   ? ,

16 Here are six synonyms of the word 'frail':

brittle, feeble, vulnerable, decrepit, weak, breakable

Take one letter from each word, in order, to spell out a further synonym of the word 'frail'.

17 Which word inside the brackets is closest in meaning to the word in capital letters?

OSTRACISE (flaunt, appal, banish, beleaguer, chastise)

18 One man can dig a trench in 2 hours
A second man can dig a trench in 3 hours
A third man can dig a trench in 5 hours
A fourth man can dig a trench in 6 hours

How many hours will it take to dig a trench if they all work together at their own speeds?

0.43, 0.63, 0.83, 1.03, 1.23

19 Underline which of these five words goes together with struck, chart and gazer.

worm, **stage**, wars, dance, law

20 If Balaclava is to hat, then burnous is to which of these?

scarf, tie, hood, belt, shoe

21 Which word inside the brackets is always part of the word outside the brackets?

ZAPATEADO (whispering, sliding, clicking, swimming, climbing)

22 Solve the anagram (one word):

nose crane

23 To which of the five boxes A, B, C, D or E, can a dot be added so that both dots meet the same conditions as in the box on the left?

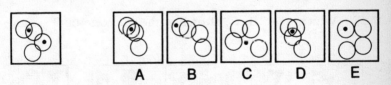

A   B   C   D   E

24 Insert the missing number.

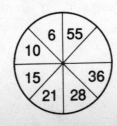

25 Which of the following is not a tree?

APPLRO
IWWOLL
RECYHR
OLIVET

26 Which of A, B, C, D or E is the odd one out?

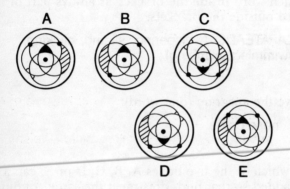

27 Which of A, B, C, D or E is the odd one out?

28 Insert the missing number.

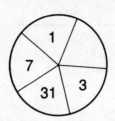

29 Fill in the missing word.

DIVE (DERISIVE) RISE
CORN (. . . . .) SAID

30 Which word inside the brackets is never part of the word outside the brackets?

MAUD (shepherd, woollen, plaid, Welsh)

31 Which word means the same as gelid?

pink, soft, cold, warm, jelly

32 Solve the anagram (one word):

reamer tap

33 Place a word in the brackets which means the same as the words outside the brackets.

balk (. . .) shy

34 What is a lazar? Is it:

(a) an Egyptian (b) a beam (c) a leper
(d) a churchman (e) a bazaar?

35 Which of squares A to H is the missing one?

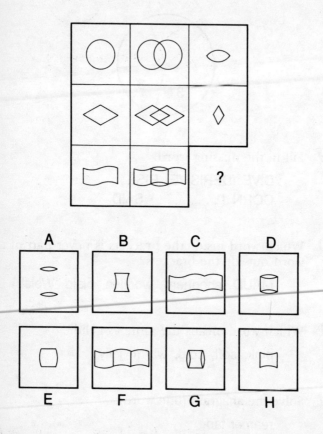

A
B
C
D

E
F
G
H

142

36

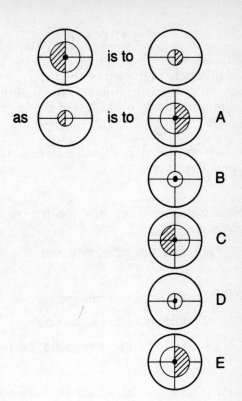

37

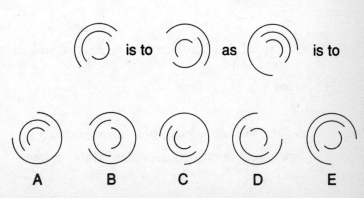

A   B   C   D   E

38   A B C D E F G H

Which letter is four to the right of the letter immediately to the left of the letter immediately to the left of the letter which is three to the right of the letter immediatly to the left of the letter B?

39   Which word means a small island, a solution and an operating lever?

40   Place two three-letter 'bits' together to equal a narrow opening.

> kni, cra, pru, che, nny, vat

41   Which word is part of this group?

> emerald, garnet, topaz, opal

Choose from: terrine, marcasite, porringer, tureen

42   Underline the words which are opposite to each other.

> ghostly, wiry, frangible, unbreakable, paramount

43   Insert a word that completes the first word and starts the second word.

> nut .... jack

44   Underline the two words which mean the same.

> principal, fortnight, quotidian, daily, prefect

45

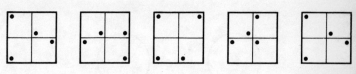

Which option below continues the sequence above?

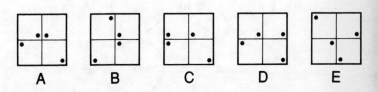

46 Which word inside the brackets is closest in meaning to the word in capital letters?

GRATUITY (payment, reward, freedom, appreciation, present)

47 Which word means the same as the two words outside the brackets?

embed (. . .) group

48 Nurture is to deprive as intrepid is to:

doughty, flinching, homely, charitable, submissive

49

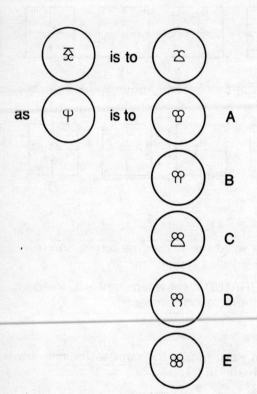

50 Which of the tiles A to H will fit logically into the space?

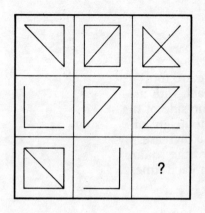

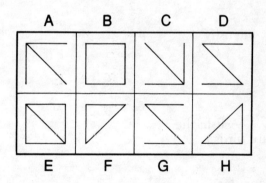

Answers Test 7

1 G.

2 D. (There are four triangles each with its base on one side of the square. The height of the triangle increases by a quarter of the square side length each time.

3 15. (19 − 4 and 17 − 2.)

4 subside, intensify

5 husk

6 lamprey. (A fish; the others are birds.)

7 21. (Triangular numbers.
$$4 + 3 + 2 + 1 = 10$$
$$5 + 4 + 3 + 2 + 1 = 15$$
$$6 + 5 + 4 + 3 + 2 + 1 = 21$$
etc.)

8 submissive

9 B. (The right side is folded back on to the left.)

10 Maya. (The others are African tribes.)

11 NOVICE. (The words have consonant and vowel alternately.)

12 race

13 C. (Vertically and horizontally: the arms with the small black circle and the arrowhead both advance 180° each time; the arm with the small white circle advances 90° and that with the cross bar advances 135°, each time.)

14 D. (Each side of the triangle, in turn, is curved out and then, in turn, curved in.

15 430. (i.e. 4.30. They are times, each advancing 45 minutes, shown without the 'dot'.)

16 tender

17 banish

18 0.83 hours. (Which is ⅚ hour or 50 minutes.)

19 wars. (All four words can have the prefix 'star'.)

20 hood

21 clicking

22 resonance

23 B. (So that one dot is in one circle only and one dot is in two circles only.)

24 45. (Start at 6 and, moving round anticlockwise, add 4, then 5, then 6, etc.

25 OLIVET. (Anagram of VIOLET. The trees are poplar, willow and cherry.)

26 B. (A and D, C and E, are the same, but rotated.)

27 B. (The others are the same figure rotated.)

28 15. (Start at 1 and moving round clockwise, jump alternate sections, doubling and adding one.)

29 SARDONIC. (Anagrams.)

30 Welsh

31 cold

32 parameter

33 jib

34 (c)

35 B. (The middle
segment of the central
column is taken out,
turned around and
put into the right
column.)

36 E.

37 C. (The longer curve
moves 90° clockwise.
The two smaller
curves move through
180°.)

38 F.

39 key

40 cranny

41 marcasite

42 frangible, unbreakable

43 cracker

44 quotidian, daily

45 D. (The dot in each small square follows its own sequence.)

46 reward

47 set

48 flinching

49 E. (The shapes in the circles represent the numbers 3, 2, 9 and 8, backed by their reflections.)

50 A. (Column 1 is added to Column 2 and lines common to both are deleted to make Column 3. similarly for the Rows.)

Scoring Chart for Test 7

20–24	Average
25–29	Good
30–39	Very Good
40–44	Excellent
45–50	Exceptional

TEST 8

1 Which of A, B, C, D or E is the odd one out?

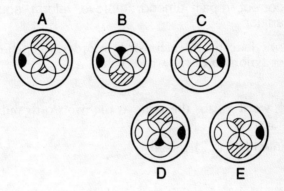

2 Which of the boxes A, B, C, D or E, has least in common with the box on the left?

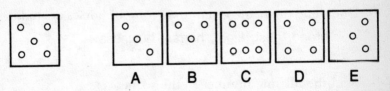

3 180 is to (9, 15, 20) as 84 is to:

(2, 6, 12), (3, 4, 12), (3, 4, 7), (6, 12, 8), (6, 7, 21)

4 Here are seven synonyms of the word 'rectify':

correct, repair, amend, improve, reform, square, adjust

Take one letter from each word, in order, to spell out a further synonym of the word 'rectify'.

5 Which word means the same as the two words outside the brackets?

intend (. . . .) miserly

6 Which word means the opposite of quiescence?

querying, disagreement, repose, activity, agreement

7 Underline the name given to a group of horses at stud.

brood, grist, flight, harras, business

8 Find the missing number in the sequence:

192, 221, ? , 285, 320,

9 Underline the word which is the odd one out.

pinnace, phaeton, currach, pontoon, gondola

10

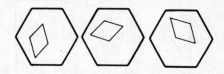

Which option below continues the sequence above?

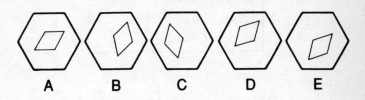

| A | B | C | D | E |

11 Which word inside the brackets is closest in meaning to the word in capital letters?

SYLLABUS (adolescent, vehicle, study, curriculum, idiot)

12 Which word is the odd one out?

tarn, mere, stream, lock, lake

13 Which of the tiles A to H will fit logically into the space?

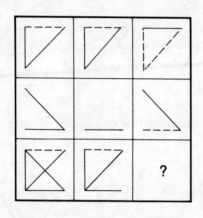

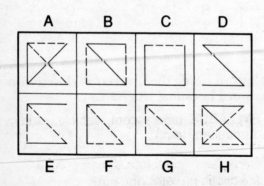

14 Which of A, B, C, D or E is the odd one out?

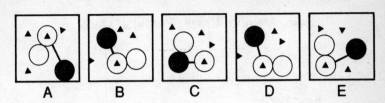

A   B   C   D   E

15 Read clockwise to find a word in each circle. You have to provide the missing letters. The two words are synonyms.

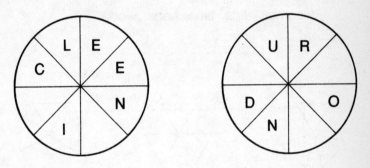

16 Underline the two words which are opposite in meaning.

clamorous, moderate, tiny, voracious, susceptible, sardonic

17 What is the next number in this sequence?

7, 27, 58, 102,   ? ,

18 Which word inside the brackets is always a part of the word outside the brackets?

WORSTED (spots, wool, cotton, stripes, linen)

19 If Everest is to Himalayas, then Sierra Madre is to which of these?

Spain, Mexico, Brazil, Portugal, Chile

20 Solve the anagram (one word):

tune hopes

21 Underline which of these five words goes with stead, help and run.

corner, slide, time, hope, work

22

Which option below continues the sequence above?

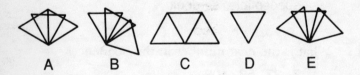

A   B   C   D   E

23 Insert the missing number.

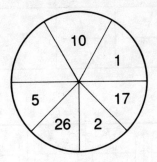

24 Insert the word that completes the first word and starts the second word.

prim . . . . bud

25 Which of the tiles A to H will fit logically into the space?

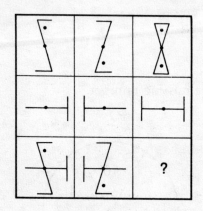

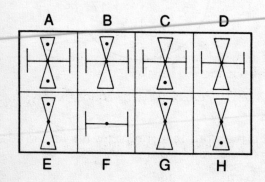

26 Which of these is the odd one out?

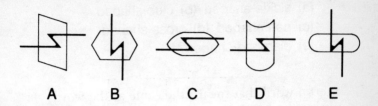

A   **B**   **C**   **D**   **E**

27 Which word means a tool, a drink and a blow?

28 Which word below goes with able, maker and time?

safe, ship, dive, tight, fully

29 Insert the same number twice into this equation as it stands, to make it correct.

16 × 2 = 8

30 Which word inside the brackets is never part of the word outside the brackets?

METHEGLIN (Welsh, liquor, honey, rum)

31 Solve the anagram (one word):

I rue ranch

32 Which word means the same as pensile?

horizontal, upright, hanging, prolonged, extensive

33 What is falcate? Is it:

(a) sickle-shaped (b) club-shaped
(c) pea-shaped (d) cross-shaped
(e) diamond-shaped?

34 Insert a word that means the same as the words outside the brackets.

bunting (. . . .) droop

35

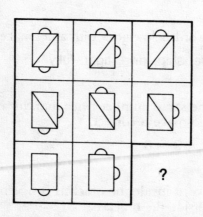

?

Which of squares A to H is the missing one?

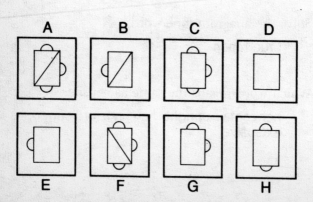

36

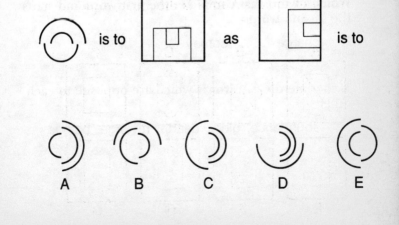

37

38 Insert the word that means the same as the definitions outside the brackets.

furnace (. . . . .) advance steadily

39 Connoisseur is to expert as vintner is to:

producer, merchant, wine, waiter, bottler

40 Underline the two words which mean the same:

invexed, depleted, diffident, pacify, concave

41 Which word continues this list?

Drake, Raleigh, Beatty, Nelson

Choose from: Brambell, Jellicoe, Hess, Garnett

42 Place two three-letter 'bits' together to equal a Spanish sheep.

ton, ino, lin, mer, cat, cot

43 Insert a word that completes the first word and starts the second word.

charge . . . . some

44 Underline the two words which are opposite to each other:

abundance, glory, dearth, revenge, bathos

45 Which of these is the odd one out?

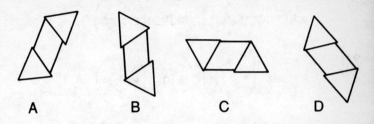

A   B   C   D

46   ONLY, TWIN, THAT, FOAM, FIST,

Which word below continues the sequence above?

TSAR, SINK, TURF, MOVE, SELF

47 Which word can be inserted in all three sets of brackets to form another word with the addition of the letters on either side of the brackets?

L (. . .) R
M (. . .) Y
H (. . .) Y

48 How many minutes before 12 a.m. is it, if one hour ago it was twice as many minutes after 9 a.m.?

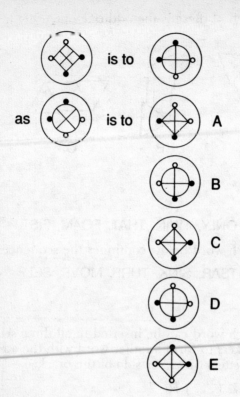

50 Which of the tiles A to H will fit logically into the space?

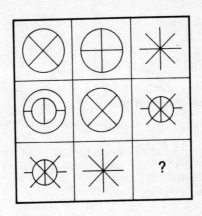

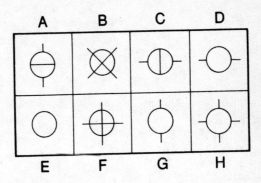

A B C D

E F G H

Answers Test 8

1 C.

2 C. (All the others are part of the figure on the left.)

3 (3, 4, 7). (84 is the smallest number into which these three numbers will divide.)

4 redress

5 mean

6 activity

7 harras

8 252. (This is $(16^2 - 4)$. The sequence is $(14^2 - 4)$, $(15^2 - 4)$, $(16^2 - 4)$, $(17^2 - 4)$, $(18^2 - 4)$.)

9 phaeton

10 B. (The hexagon rolls over on to each base in turn.)

11 curriculum

12 stream. (The others are still water.)

13 H. (Column 1 is added to Column 2 to make Column 3. Where two dashed lines coincide, they become full lines; where two full lines coincide they become dashed. Similarly for the Rows.)

14 C. (The empty circle is touching the black circle. In all the others it touches the other white circle.)

15 ENCIRCLE, SURROUND

16 moderate, voracious

17 161. (The differences between the numbers are consecutive squares less 5. That is, the differences are: $5^2 - 5$, $6^2 - 5$, $7^2 - 5$, $8^2 - 5$.)

18 wool

19 Mexico

20 penthouse

21 work. (The four words can all have the prefix 'home')

22 C. The bottom two triangles are swinging upwards an equal amount at a time.

23 37. (Starting at 1 and moving clockwise, jump alternate sectors adding odd numbers, i.e. 1, 3, 5, 7, 9, 11.)

24 rose

25 A.

26 C. (In all the others the 'lightning bolt' goes through the narrowest part of the figure.)

27 punch

28 fully. (The four words can all be prefixed with the word 'peace'.)

29 $16 \times 32 = 8^3$

30 rum

31 hurricane

32 hanging

33 (a)

34 flag

35 D. (Horizontally and vertically, only lines common to the first two squares are carried forward to the third square.)

36 B.

37 C.

38 forge

39 merchant

40 concave, invexed

41 Jellicoe

42 merino

43 hand

44 abundance, dearth

45 B. (All the others are the same figure rotated.)

46 SINK. (The first two letters of each word are the first two letters of the numbers ONE, TWO, THREE, etc.)

47 ONE

48 40 minutes.

49 C.

50 A. (The first column is placed on top of the second column. Lines in common disappear and remaining lines are placed in the third column. Similarly for the rows.)

Scoring Chart for Test 8

20-24   Average
25-29   Good
30-39   Very Good
40-44   Excellent
45-50   Exceptional

Total scoring chart for the eight tests

160–199　Average
200–239　Good
240–319　Very Good
320–359　Excellent
360–400　Exceptional